FIRST FIELD
INSECTS
OF SOUTHERN AFRICA

ALAN WEAVING

Contents

What is an insect?   3

Insect growth and
    metamorphosis   4

Grouping and identifying
    insects   6

Collecting and keeping
    insects   8

How to use this book   9

Key to insect orders   10

Species accounts   12

Glossary   56

Index and checklist   57

Swallowtail, *Papilio colonna*

First edition published in 1999 by
Struik Publishers
(a division of New Holland
Publishing (South Africa) (Pty) Ltd)
80 McKenzie Street,
Cape Town, 8001, South Africa

New Holland Publishing is a member
of Johnnic Communications Ltd.
Visit us at **www.struik.co.za**

Log on to our photographic website
www.imagesofafrica.co.za for an
African experience.

6 8 10 9 7 5

Editor: Gary Lyon
Designer: Dominic Robson
Proofreader: Cara Cilliers

Reproduction by
Disc Express Cape (Pty) Ltd
Printed and bound by
Times Offset (M) Sdn Bhd

ISBN 1 86872 292 9

What is an insect?

Insects belong to a group of animals known as arthropods, which also includes spiders, scorpions, millipedes, centipedes, mites, ticks and crabs. All arthropods have a hard outside skeleton (called an exoskeleton), and jointed legs. Their bodies are divided into parts or segments. Insects are immediately recognisable because their bodies have three sections, the head, thorax and abdomen. The head has a pair of large compound eyes^G, a pair of feelers, known as antennae^G, and the mouthparts. The thorax, or middle segment of the body, bears the legs and wings. It has six jointed legs and, usually, four wings. Some insects have only two wings, others none at all. The abdomen may end in two or three tails (cerci^G).

The abdomen of a male insect ends in a pair of claspers which are used for mating; females have a single egg-laying tube, known as an ovipositor^G.

Longicorn, *Zographus niveosparsus*

Insect growth and metamorphosis

Because of their hard external skeletons, insects cannot grow unless they change their old skeleton for a new, larger one that forms underneath it. This is known as moulting. When an insect moults, the old skeleton splits down the back and the insect crawls out and puffs itself up to stretch the new, still-soft skeleton to its maximum size before it hardens. This provides space for the insect to grow.

After hatching from their eggs, young insects moult several times, growing at intervals. As they moult, the young insects undergo a change or metamorphosis, until they reach the adult state.

Incomplete metamorphosis

The young of some insects are similar in appearance to the adults: only slight changes take place at each moult. Their wing buds develop on the outside of their protective external skeleton, becoming more obvious at each moult. These young or developing insects are called nymphs, and are said to be *hemimetabolous*, as they have an incomplete or simple metamorphosis.

Complete metamorphosis

In other insects, the young look totally different from the adults. They are called larvae (caterpillars, grubs or maggots) and will pass through a resting stage, or pupa^G, during which their wings develop within their protective external skeletons. They emerge later, as adults, from this protective outer covering. All these insects are *holometabolous* as they undergo a complete change or metamorphosis.

Antlion larva, Myrmeleontidae

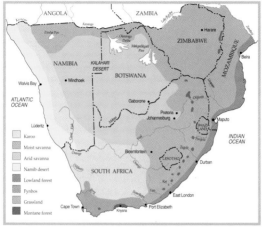

Grouping and identifying insects

The animal kingdom is divided into several groups known as phyla, with members of each phylum having certain features in common. Phyla are each divided into classes, orders, families, genera and, finally, into species. Insects belong to the phylum Arthropoda.

A species is a single type of organism where individuals of that type breed only with others of the same kind to produce fertile offspring. A species may or may not have a common name but always has a scientific name which has two parts, the genus name and the species name. Scientific names are preferable to common names because the latter are often different in different countries or even parts of the same country, or may refer only to a whole group such as a family or a genus.

Jewel Beetle, *Sternocera orissa*

Caterpillar of *Papilio demodocus*

The full classification of a Robber Fly, *Lamyra gulo*:

Phylum	Arthropoda
Class	Insecta
Subclass	Pterygota
Division	Endopterygota
Order	Diptera
Suborder	Brachycera
Family	Asilidae
Subfamily	Laphriinae
Tribe	Laphriini
Genus	*Lamyra*
Species	*gulo*

Identifying insects to species level can be difficult, and often needs specialist knowledge, some rather complicated scientific keys, and a microscope. However, it is quite possible, with practise, to identify the *order* to which an insect belongs, using a simple key.

The basic key (p. 10) refers only to adults since juvenile forms may often look totally different or simply have no wings. Many winged insect species have lost the power of flight and adults have very reduced wings or none at all. This may apply to females only or to both sexes. Some creatures, such as scale insects, do not look like insects at all. In spite of these exceptions, the key should be quite useful as an insect identification tool, in the field.

Robber Fly, *Lamyra gulo*

Collecting and keeping insects

Insects occur almost anywhere and therefore are relatively easy for an enthusiast to find. Those that fly can be caught with a net; so too can those that live in grass and other low-growing vegetation. All sorts of traps can be used to attract and catch insects, a light trap for night-flying insects, for example, or a container baited with dung for dung beetles. Simply turning over stones or logs can also be productive, but remember to return these to their original position in case you have disrupted someone's home.

If you are planning on making an insect collection, your specimens should be handled carefully and killed in the right (and humane) way. A small jar with some tissue or plaster of paris on the bottom, moistened with a few drops of ethyl acetate (available at pharmacies), is effective in killing many kinds of insects. Each specimen should then be mounted on a special pin and fixed on a setting board with the wings and legs suitably arranged.

The insect must be left for several days to dry out and stiffen. If the collection is to have any value at all, each specimen must have a label attached below it on the same pin, giving details of where and when the insect was caught. If possible, include the latitude and longitude of the locality, in degrees and minutes, and the name of the collector. Any other information can be written on a second label.

Generally, insects are not easy to keep alive, simply because we do not know enough about their diets or the other conditions they need for survival. Many need more space than can easily be provided. Caterpillars are a notable exception, just as long as you know their correct food plant. Also, some insects which have a varied diet, such as cockroaches, and others such as Parktown prawns and some of the ground-living beetles, can be kept alive, at least for a while. Captive insects must always have plenty of air and fresh food, and must not be allowed to dry out.

How to use this book

When you find an insect use the simple key on pp. 10–11 to find which order or group it belongs to. Then turn to the relevant page to learn more about that insect group. The larger orders have several entries. Some insects that you try to key out may not belong to any of the groups dealt with here. If you want to go any further, you will then have to turn to more detailed books.

Each group dealt with here is described according to the headings:

Names The English and Afrikaans names are given along with the order, family and subfamily to which each insect group belongs.

Size Gives the body length and/or wingspan in millimetres.

Number of species This is a rough figure for the number of known species in southern African.

Identification Describes the characteristic features typical of that insect group.

Where found The habitat or environment in which the insect is likely to be found.

Habits Describes aspects of behaviour such as feeding, reproduction and defence.

Food The diet of the adult, larval and/or nymphal stages.

Life history Describes the life history of the insect during its metamorphosis into the adult.

Similar species Highlights insect groups that share similar features.

Any word followed by a small ^G is defined in the glossary on p. 56.

Termites, *Trinervitermes* sp.

KEY TO INSECT ORDERS

Page numbers indicate where species accounts begin for each order.

Page

1. INSECTS OBVIOUSLY WITHOUT ANY WINGS

1. Narrow-waisted, ant-like

    A. Black, brown or yellowish ⸺ **Ants (workers, soldiers)**   55

    B. Conspicuously coloured red and black with white markings

    ⸺ **Velvet Ants (females)****

2. Neither narrow-waisted, nor ant-like

    A. Parasites on birds or mammals ⸺ **Fleas, Lice****

    B. Not parasitic

        a. Abdomen with 2 or 3 thread-like tails

        ⸺ **Fishmoths/Silverfish****

        b. Abdomen with a pair of tubes (cornicles) ⸺ **Aphids**   28

        c. Abdomen without tails

            i. Whitish, soft-bodied insects with large heads

            ⸺ **Termites (workers, soldiers)**   14

            ii. Elongate, stick-like bodies ⸺ **Stick Insects (some)**   22

            iii. Hind-legs well developed for jumping

            Grasshoppers (some, mostly females)   20

            iv. Flattened, oval-shaped, with shield covering head

            ⸺ **Cockroaches (some)**   13

    C. Scale-like or globular; no obvious legs; immobile or very slow-moving; unlike insects at all ⸺ **Mealybugs and Scale insects****

2. INSECTS WITH WINGS, BUT NOT OBVIOUS WHEN FOLDED

1. Fore-wings thickened towards base, membranous near tip

    ⸺ **Bugs (order Hemiptera; suborder Heteroptera)**   23

2. Fore-wings hardened uniformly to form covers for hind-wings, sometimes permanently fused together in midline. If reduced, they usually cover the hind-wings completely

    A. No pincers at end of abdomen ⸺ **Beetles**   31

    B. Pair of pincers at end of abdomen ⸺ **Earwigs**   16

3. Fore-wings reduced, only partly covering hind-wings

    ⸺ **Stick Insects (some)**   22

3. INSECTS WITH OBVIOUS WINGS

Page

1. Two wings ———————————————— **Flies** 44

2. Four wings

   A. Wings hairy ———————— **Caddisflies****

   B. Wings covered with scales ———— **Butterflies, Moths** 49

   C. Wings without scales

      a. Fore-wings thickened and often smaller than the membranous hind-wings.

         i. Legs uniformly developed ———— **Cockroaches** 13

         ii. Fore-legs adapted for catching prey

            —————————— **Praying Mantids** 15

         iii. Hind-legs adapted for jumping

            ———— **Katydids, Crickets, Grasshoppers** 17

      b. Fore-and hind-wings membranous, transparent or coloured, with or without dark markings

         i. Fore-wings of similar size to hind-wings

            i.i. Wings held out sideways ———— **Dragonflies** 12

            or lengthwise along body ———— **Damselflies** 12

            i.ii. Wings held tent-wise over body

            i.ii.a. Legs uniformly developed ———— **Antlions** 30

                —————— **Lacewings, Alderflies****

            i.ii.b. Fore-legs adapted for catching prey

                ————————————— **Mantidflies****

            i.iii. Wings held flat over body ———— **Termites (winged)** 14

            —————————— (no icon shown) **Stoneflies,**

                         Scorpionflies**

         ii. Fore-wings mostly larger than hind-wings

            ii.i. Wings held vertically over body ———— **Mayflies****

            ii.ii. Wings held tentwise over body ———— **Bugs** 28

         (order Hemiptera; suborder Homoptera)

         (includes winged Aphids or Greenflies)

            ii.iii. Wings held flat over body

            ———————— **Wasps, Bees, winged Ants** 50

** not included in this guide

Dragonflies and Damselflies

Order Odonata

Afrikaans name: Naaldekokers.

Size: Length 20–115 mm; wingspan 20–140 mm.

Number of species: 209

Identification: Fast-flying, often brightly coloured insects. Head with very small antennae[G] and huge eyes. Four similar-sized, gauze-like wings, which at rest are held out sideways in dragonflies and beside the abdomen in damsel-flies. The legs are forwardly placed, bristly and clawed to catch prey.

Where found: Usually near water.

Habits: Active during the day, perching on prominent viewpoints and darting after prey. They mate in a 'wheel' position. The female lays her eggs in water either while flying or when perched on semi-submerged vegetation, sometimes while she is still joined to the male.

Food: Adults eat flying insects; nymphs eat water insects, tadpoles and small fish.

Life history: Nymphs (naiads) live in fresh water. Prey is caught with an extendible lower lip. Oxygen is absorbed through gills located inside the rectum (dragonflies) or through leaf-like gills at the end of the abdomen (damselflies). Mature nymphs crawl onto a plant stem or rock and the adult emerges.

Similar insects: Adult antlions, which are much weaker fliers, and whose wings are folded roof-wise over the abdomen.

Trithemis arteriosa

Cockroaches

Order Blattodea

Afrikaans name: Kakkerlakke.

Size: Length 5–50 mm.

Number of species: 175

Identification: Flattened insects with long bristly legs. The head has long, swept-back antennae[G], and is covered by a large shield-like plate. Fore-wings are leathery, overlapping when folded flat over the abdomen. Some species, especially the females, have no wings. The tip of the abdomen has a pair of cerci[G].

Where found: Native species are found under stones, logs, in leaf litter and under bark. Introduced species are found in buildings, especially kitchens, where they are regarded as pests.

Habits: Usually concealed by day, emerging at night to feed. Native species may feed in leaf litter during the day. Species with wings are often attracted to light at night.

Food: Plants, dead leaves and human food.

Life history: Females lay from 5–60 or more eggs in a purse-like package, which may remain protruding from the female's abdomen until the nymphs hatch. Others give birth to live young. Nymphs look like small wingless adults.

Similar insects: Some plant bugs, but these have piercing mouthparts. Also some beetles, although the front wings of beetles do not overlap when they are folded.

Deropeltis wahlbergi

Termites

Order Isoptera

Afrikaans name: Termiete.

Size: Length 3–20 mm.

Number of species: 215

Identification: Termites live in large colonies. They are creamy-white, soft-bodied insects with relatively large brown heads, and straight, bead-like antennae[G]. The body has no waist. Reproductive males and females ('flying ants') have four similar-sized wings that are shed after a brief flight. Soldiers have large mandibles, or snouts for squirting or spraying defensive liquids.

Where found: In wood, in nests built above or below ground, or in trees. May attack timber in houses.

Habits: They forage for food from the cover of earthen runways which they build on the ground, on the trunks of trees, or in the open.

Food: Grass, humus, dead wood, dry manure and paper.

Trinervitermes sp.

Life history: After shedding their wings, males and females pair up and search for new nest sites. Only the queen lays eggs. Nymphs hatch from the eggs, and develop either into workers, or into winged males or females (called alates) which leave the nest to mate.

Similar insects: Ants, which are mostly dark coloured, have waists between the thorax and abdomen, and elbowed antennae[G].

Praying Mantids

Order Mantodea

Afrikaans name: Hottentotsgotte.

Size: Length 20–125 mm.

Number of species: 120

Identification: Strong, spiny fore-legs adapted for catching and holding prey, held folded as if in prayer when at rest. Their heads are triangular and very mobile, with large eyes and thread-like antennae[G]. The fore-wings are leathery and fold flat over the abdomen. Females of some species are wingless. Often green or brown in colour, and may mimic leaves, twigs, grass heads or bark. Body and legs may have leaf-like outgrowths (extensions) to improve camouflage.

Where found: Among vegetation, on flowers, on tree trunks, or on the ground.

Habits: Remain motionless, waiting in ambush for prey. Often walk with a swaying motion when disturbed. Commonly attracted to light at night.

Food: Other insects.

Life history: Eggs are laid in a frothy capsule which hardens on drying. The capsule is attached to plants or stones, or is hidden in a hole in the ground. Nymphs have no wings and usually curve their abdomens over their backs.

Similar insects: Mantid flies (not included in this guide), which fold their wings in a roof-wise manner over the abdomen.

Miomantis sp.

Earwigs

Order Dermaptera

Afrikaans name: Oorkruipers.

Size: Length 8–50 mm.

Number of species: 38

Identification: Easily recognised by a pair of pincers at the end of the abdomen. The body is elongate, usually brownish in colour. The head has thread-like antennae[G]. Hind-wings are large and ear-shaped when open; when closed they are tightly folded below the short, hardened fore-wings. Some species are wingless.

Where found: Underneath stones, logs and bark.

Habits: They remain hidden during the day, coming out to feed at night. Pincers may be used for catching prey or in defence; and also to help fold the hind-wings.

Food: Plant material, dead and living insects.

Life history: Females lay their eggs in burrows dug in soil and guard them until they hatch. They care for their young. The young look like small, paler adults without wings.

Similar insects: Rove beetles (not included in this guide) (order Coleoptera; family Staphylinidae), which do not have pincers at the end of the abdomen.

Forficula senegalensis

Bush Katydids

Order Orthoptera (family: Tettigoniidae; Phaneropterinae)

Afrikaans name: Langasempies.

Size: Length 20–90 mm.

Number of species: 100

Identification: Bush katydids have long, filamentous antennae[G] with more than 30 segments each, and these are often longer than their bodies. Hind-legs are long and moderately developed for jumping. Fore-wings are usually elongate, green and leaf-like, with a file and scraper for producing songs, and are folded roof-wise over the abdomen. They have ears on the fore-legs. The female has a long, scimitar-shaped ovipositor[G].

Where found: Among the foliage of bushes and trees, or on the ground.

Habits: Usually concealed during the day; active at night, when they are often attracted to light. They are the cause of much of the insect noise you hear at night.

Food: Leaves and flowers. Some species are predatory.

Life history: The male attracts females with loud calls. The female lays her eggs in plant tissue, inserting her ovipositor[G] into stems or the edges of leaves, or in the ground. Nymphs look like small adults without wings.

Similar insects: Grasshoppers, which have shorter antennae[G] with less than 30 segments; crickets, which are brown or black, the females with needle-like ovipositors[G].

Phaneroptera sp.

Armoured Ground Crickets

Order Orthoptera (family: Tettigoniidae; Hetrodinae)

Afrikaans name: Koringkriek.

Size: Length 20–45 mm.

Number of species: At least 12.

Identification: They have long, thread-like antennae^G, a large spiny thorax and a rounded, somewhat soft abdomen. The colour is greenish or brown.

Where found: On the ground, or in bushes in drier areas.

Habits: Armoured ground crickets crawl about looking for food. They ooze foul repellant liquid if attacked or handled.

Acanthoplus sp.

Food: Omnivorous, eating plants, dead and living insects.

Life history: The female digs a hole in the ground with the tip of her abdomen, in which she lays 6–15 eggs. The hole is then filled in. The young look like small adults.

Similar insects: Parktown prawns (not included in this guide) (family Stenopelmatidae) and related species, which are nocturnal, do not have spiny bodies, and have grotesque faces. The female has a long, curved ovipositor^G.

Acanthoplus sp.

Crickets

Order Orthoptera (family: Gryllidae)

Afrikaans name: Krieke.

Size: Length 10–70 mm.

Number of species: 70

Identification: Cricket antennae[G] are often longer than their bodies, and have more than 30 segments each. There are two unsegmented cerci[G] at the end of the abdomen. The hind-legs are strongly developed for jumping. Specially adapted fore-wings are rubbed together to produce loud chirping songs, and also act as sound reflectors. Wings fold to form a box-like cover over the abdomen. The female has a long, needle-like ovipositor[G] which she uses to lay her eggs.

Where found: Beneath logs or stones, or in burrows in the ground. Some are found in trees.

Habits: Crickets spend the day concealed in hiding places, emerging at night to feed. They often enter houses.

Food: Omnivorous.

Life history: Eggs are laid singly in the ground or in plant tissue. Nymphs are miniatures of adults but have no wings.

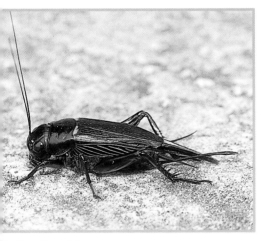

Gryllus bimaculatus

Bush Locusts

Order Orthoptera (family: Pyrgomorphidae)

Afrikaans name:
Bosstinksprinkaan.

Size: Length 12–86 mm.

Number of species: 39

Identification: Antennae[G] are much shorter than the body and have less than 30 segments. Hind-legs are well developed for jumping. Fore-wings are tougher and narrower than hind-wings. Wings may be present or absent, or just reduced. The female does not have a long ovipositor[G]. Many species are brightly coloured. Bush locusts seldom stridulate[G].

Where found: In bushes or on herbaceous plants, sometimes on the ground.

Habits: Bush locusts are sluggish, and produce a foul-smelling foam in defense when handled. They also fan open and rustle their brightly coloured wings if attacked.

Food: Plants, mostly dicotyledons[G].

Phymateus viridipes

Life history: Eggs are laid in the ground. Nymphs are gregarious, often seen in large clusters until they are almost fully grown. Some species occasionally migrate in large swarms, hence the name 'bush locusts'.

Similar insects: Acridid grass-hoppers, which are mostly cryptically[G] coloured and are much more active. Many species stridulate[G]. Acridid grasshopper nymphs are not gregarious and adults do not swarm, except for a few 'locust' species. Bush katydids, which are also cryptically coloured, but whose antennae are very long with more than 30 segments.

Grasshoppers

Order Orthoptera (family: Acrididae)

Afrikaans name: Sprinkane en treksprinkane.

Size: Length 10–87 mm.

Number of species: 356

Identification: Very varied in appearance. Often cryptically^G coloured. Antennae^G are relatively short (less than 30 segments). The hind-legs are well adapted for jumping. There are both winged and wingless species. The fore-wings are tougher and narrower than the hind-wings. There are ears on each side of the first abdominal segment.

Where found: In trees, bushes and grass, sometimes on the ground.

Habits: Active during the day. Many species stridulate^G, rubbing a row of small pegs on the inner face of

the femur^G against the hardened edge of the fore-wing.

Food: Leaves and grass.

Life history: Eggs are laid in the ground; the female digs with the tip of her abdomen. Nymphs are similar to the adults but do not have wings.

Similar insects: Bush locusts which are sluggish and brightly coloured; other families of short-horned grasshoppers (not included in this guide). Katydids are also cryptically coloured, but their antennae^G are very long with more than 30 segments each.

Acanthacris sp.

Stick Insects

Order Phasmatodea

Afrikaans name: Stokinsekte.

Size: Length 10–250 mm.

Number of species: 50

Phasmatidae

Identification: Very long, thin, stick-like bodies; all legs are long and thin. Some species are winged fore-wings are much smaller than the fan-shaped hind-wings.

Where found: In bushes and trees also in grass. Sometimes attracted to light.

Habits: Motionless during the day moving about at night to feed. If disturbed they may drop to the ground and feign death. Winged species flash their brightly coloured hind-wings in self-defence. Fore-legs are held out together in front of the insect, adding to the stick effect.

Food: Plants.

Life history: Eggs are dropped singly onto the ground. Nymphs are miniatures of adults, but lack wings.

Similar insects: Some praying mantids, which are distinguishable by their raptorial[G] fore-legs.

Assassin Bugs

Order Hemiptera (suborder: Heteroptera; family: Reduviidae)

Afrikaans name: Roofwantse.

Size: Length 7–30 mm.

Number of species: 328

Identification: Oval to oblong in shape. Colour brownish or black, many species with bright warning colours. The stout, curved proboscis[G] has a sharp point and is usually folded back below the head. The fore-legs may be adapted for catching prey.

Where found: In all kinds of vegetation, including flowers. Some habitually remain on the ground, sheltering below stones and logs during the day.

Habits: Assassin bugs ambush their prey, stalking to within striking distance. They are sometimes attracted to light at night when they may inflict painful bites in self-defence if handled.

Food: Other insects.

Life history: Eggs are laid in clusters on leaf foliage or some other substrate. Nymphs resemble the adults.

Acanthaspis obscura

Squash Bugs/Twig Wilters

Order Hemiptera (suborder: Heteroptera; family: Coreidae)

Afrikaans name:
Blaarpootwantse, verwelkbesies.

Size: Length 5–40 mm.

Number of species: 150

Identification: Dull-coloured stout bugs with prominent hind-legs, often with spines and leaf-like expansions. Abdomen and sometimes thorax may be expanded to the side.

Where found:
Vegetation, especially on young shoots.

Habits: They are alert bugs, flying readily. They secrete a foul-smelling liquid if handled, larger species squirting it for some distance.

Food: Plant juices or sap.

Life history: Clusters of eggs are attached to plants. Nymphs resemble adults, but unlike the adults they have no wings.

Holopterna alata

Shield Bugs

Order Hemiptera (suborder: Heteroptera; family: Pentatomidae)

Afrikaans name: Skildstinkbesies.

Size: Length 4–25 mm.

Number of species: 308

Identification: Shield bugs are round or shield-shaped, commonly greenish or brownish in colour. The triangular shield between the wings is well developed; the corners of the pronotum^G are often pointed.

Where found: Any vegetation.

Nymphs^G surrounding egg mass

Shield Bug adult

Habits: These insects produce very strong-smelling secretions when disturbed. They are sometimes attracted to light.

Food: The juices or sap of foliage, stems and fruit; some species suck body fluids from caterpillars.

Life history: Eggs are barrel-shaped and laid in small clusters on foliage. Nymphs are round, often brightly coloured, without wings.

Water Striders/Pond Skaters

Order Hemiptera (suborder: Heteroptera; family: Gerridae)

Afrikaans name: Waterlopers.

Size: Length 5–20 mm.

Number of species: 10

Identification: These are dark brown, elongate insects with very long, thin mid- and hind-legs; fore-legs are short.

Where found: On the surface of pools and streams.

Gerris sp.

Habits: Water striders skate about on the water surface, supported by surface tension, looking for dead or living insects trapped in the surface film, or aquatic insects just below the surface.

Food: Other insects.

Life history: Eggs are laid in a slime-covered mass attached to water plants just below the surface.

Gerris sp.

Water Scorpions

Order Hemiptera (suborder: Heteroptera; family: Nepidae)

Afrikaans name: Waterskerpioene.

Size: Length 20–40 mm, excluding breathing tube.

Number of species: 3

Identification: They are elongate, brownish bugs with a very long breathing tube at the end of the abdomen. The scissor-like fore-legs are adapted for catching prey.

Where found: In ponds; often appear in swimming pools.

Habits: Water scorpions crawl about on the bottom of the pool or amongst water plants or wait motionless for prey to come within reach. They are sometimes attracted to light.

Food: Aquatic insects, tadpoles, other aquatic animals.

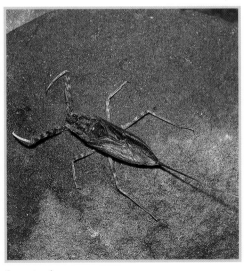

Laccotrephes sp.

Life history: Eggs are inserted into the tissues of water plants. Nymphs resemble adults but they do not have wings.

Similar insects: Water bugs (Belostomatidae) (not included in this guide), which are more robust. Some are very large, with a much shorter breathing tube. They also swim more actively.

Aphids/Plantlice/Greenflies

Order Hemiptera (suborder: Homoptera; family: Aphididae)

Afrikaans name: Plantluise.

Size: 1–6 mm.

Number of species: 125

Identification: Small, pear-shaped, soft-bodied insects with long antennae[G]; usually green in colour, sometimes yellow, pink, brown or black. Winged and wingless forms occur in the same species; the former fold their wings tent-wise over the body. The abdomen ends in a short, pointed tail and has a pair of short tubes (cornicles) that secrete wax.

Where found: Plants of all kinds, especially on young shoots.

Habits: Aphids congregate on plants in dense clusters, individual insects orientating in one direction. They produce large amounts of honeydew for ants to feed on in return for some protection from predators and parasites.

Food: Plant juices.

Subfamily Aphidinae

Life history: Life cycles can vary: some aphids reproduce sexually in autumn, their offspring surviving the winter in egg form; others reproduce throughout the year, without mating. Most species give birth to live nymphs without having to mate, and can build up large numbers in a short time. Winged females are produced which disperse to new host plants when overcrowding occurs or when host plants dry up.

Comments: Aphids are serious agricultural pests. Their numbers are controlled by predators such as ladybirds, lacewings, hoverflies and parasitic wasps.

Cicadas

Order Hemiptera (suborder: Homoptera; family: Cicadidae)

Afrikaans name: Sonbesies.

Size: Length 10–50 mm.

Number of species: 139

Identification: Broad insects with large heads; four membranous wings fold roof-wise over the body. Often attractively coloured.

Where found: In trees and bushes.

Habits: Cicadas spend much of their time resting on the branches of trees, shrubs and other plants, where they feed by piercing the bark with their proboscesᴳ. Males produce shrill, rasping songs.

Nymphal skins of Cicadas

Food: Plant juices or sap.

Life history: The female uses her ovipositorᴳ to cut slits in branches and twigs, in which she lays her eggs. Nymphs drop and burrow into the ground, where they feed on the sap of plant roots. Fully grown nymphs crawl up the trunk. Adults emerge from these nymphs. Adults are very seasonal, appearing only in high summer.

Platypleura sp.

Antlions

Order Neuroptera (family: Myrmeleontidae)

Afrikaans name: Mierleeus.

Size: Length 13–80 mm.

Number of species: 130

Identification: Adults have a long, thin abdomen and four similar-sized membranous wings that fold roof-wise over the body. Wings may be clear or marked with black and yellow. Antennae^G are relatively long and jointed.

Where found: Among all kinds of vegetation.

Habits: Antlions are slow, inefficient fliers, resting among foliage during the day. They are sometimes attracted to light. Larvae (see p. 4) live in sand from where they ambush prey; some lie in wait at the bottom of small conical pits which they dig, catching insects that fall in.

Food: Adults are either predatory or feed on pollen. Larvae feed on other insects.

Adult antlion, *Myrmeleon obscurus*

Life history: Eggs are laid in the sand. When mature, larvae spin cocoons in the sand, in which they pupate^G.

Similar insects: Owlflies (not included in this guide) (Neuroptera, family Ascalaphidae), which are swift fliers and have long, clubbed antennae^G. Dragonflies and damselflies, which are swift, day-flying insects with inconspicuous antennae^G. Dragonflies hold their wings out to the side, damselflies fold their wings along the body.

Ground Beetles

Order Coleoptera (family: Carabidae)

Afrikaans name: Oogskieters.

Size: Length 3–60 mm.

Number of species: At least 1 400.

Identification: These are brown or black beetles, sometimes with contrasting yellow or white markings. They have long antennae^G, powerful jaws and well developed legs for fast running. Many species have the hardened fore-wings (wing cases) fused together and cannot fly.

Where found: Mostly on the ground, below logs and stones or among leaf litter.

Habits: Many species run around on the ground searching for prey or mates, some during the day, others at night. If attacked, they squirt pungent defensive fluids at their assailant.

Food: Mostly insects and other small invertebrates^G.

Life history: Eggs are laid in the soil, sometimes in burrows dug by the female. Larvae are active, free-living predators. When mature they pupate^G in the soil or in a sheltered place.

Similar insects: Tiger beetles (family Cicindelidae) resemble these insects but can fly.

Thermophilum decemguttatum

Tiger Beetles

Order Coleoptera (family: Cicindelidae)

Afrikaans name: Tierkewers.

Size: Length 10–70 mm.

Number of species: 150

Identification: Elongate, slightly flattened, very fast-running beetles with long slender legs. Most species have wings and fly readily. The head is broad with prominent eyes and long, slender antennae[G]. Many have bright metallic colours or are brown or black with yellow or white patterns.

Where found: On the ground in open, sunny areas, often near water.

Habits: Most active at the hottest time of the day, when they run around rapidly, searching for prey.

Food: Insects and other small invertebrates[G].

Life history: Larvae live in burrows in which they anchor themselves, blocking the entrance with their specially shaped head and prothorax[G]. Prey that comes within reach is grabbed with sharp, curved mandibles and eaten within the burrow. Pupates[G] in the soil beside the tunnel.

Similar insects: Many ground beetles (family Carabidae), some of which cannot fly.

Cicindela brevicollis

Dung Beetles

Order Coleoptera (family: Scarabaeidae; Scarabaeinae)

Afrikaans name: Miskruiers.

Size: Length 5–50 mm.

Number of species: 780

Identification: Robust beetles with rounded backs and shovel-shaped heads for cutting out pieces of dung. Usually black or brown, some are metallic green. The tibiae^G of the fore-legs are broad and are adapted for digging. Most species can fly.

Kheper nigroaeneus

Where found: On or close to fresh animal dung.

Habits: Adults bury dung as food for themselves or their larvae, either in burrows dug below the dung mass or by making balls to be rolled away for burial at a more secluded site. There are day-flying and night-flying species; the latter are often attracted to light.

Food: Dung.

Life history: Eggs are laid singly in brood balls or sausages of dung prepared and buried by the female. When mature, larvae pupate^G in the remains of the dung supply, finally emerging as adults.

Similar insects: Rhinoceros beetles (not included in this guide) (Scarabaeidae, family Dynastinae), which are large brown beetles often with conspicuous horns on the head and/or thorax; their larvae are typical 'white grubs' and feed on decaying vegetable matter, commonly in compost heaps.

Chafers

Order Coleoptera (family: Scarabaeidae; Rutelinae and Melolonthinae)

Afrikaans name: Lentekewers, komposkewers.

Size: Length 4–20 mm.

Number of species: 1 050

Identification: The night-flying beetles are brownish, with soft, fat-looking bodies. Day-flying species have bright or metallic colours. The legs end in well developed, sharp claws.

Where found: On foliage or flowers, or in the soil during the day.

Habits: Night-flying species, including the infamous 'rose chafers', emerge from hiding places at dusk and descend on plants to feed, frequently in huge numbers. Often attracted to light. Most brightly coloured day-flying species are monkey beetles (tribe Hopliini) that burrow into daisy flowers to feed.

Food: Adults feed on foliage and flowers. Larvae feed on roots and organic matter in the soil.

Life history: Eggs are laid in the soil. Larvae are C-shaped 'white grubs'. They pupate[G] in the soil when they are full grown.

Schizonycha comosa

Fruit Chafers

Order Coleoptera (family: Scarabaeidae; Cetoniinae)

Afrikaans name: Vrugtetorre.

Size: Length 10–70 mm.

Number of species: 160

Identification: Somewhat flat, hard-bodied, squarish beetles, mostly brightly coloured and beautifully marked.

Where found: Shoots, flowers and fruit, also plant stems exuding sap.

Pachnoda sinuata

Habits: Alert, day-flying beetles that readily take to the wing. Sometimes congregate in considerable numbers on flowers. Some species invade beehives to feed on honeycombs.

Food: Adults feed on nectar, ripe fruit, flowers and sap. Larvae feed on vegetable matter such as old herbivore dung or compost.

Life history: Eggs are laid in the soil. Mature larvae pupate[G] in cocoons made by gluing together plant debris and soil particles with saliva.

Plaesiorrhinella plana

Jewel Beetles

Order Coleoptera (family: Buprestidae)

Afrikaans name: Pragkewers.

Size: Length 2–50 mm.

Number of species: 1 200

Identification: Brightly coloured, often shiny, torpedo-shaped beetles with extremely hard bodies.

Where found: Flowers or branches of dead and decaying or dying trees.

Habits: Day-flying beetles, most active during the hottest time of the day, when they are very alert and difficult to catch. They often fly around the tops of trees and bushes in flower.

Food: Adults feed on pollen, nectar or foliage. Larvae feed mostly on dead wood.

Life history: Eggs are laid on dead branches and twigs. Larvae, known as 'flat-headed borers', excavate tunnels in wood to obtain food. When mature, many pupate^G just below the outer layer of bark. Larvae of a few species live in the soil, feeding on roots.

Mating Jewel Beetles, *Evides pubiventris*

Net-Winged Beetles

Order Coleoptera (family: Lycidae)

Afrikaans name: Platvlerkkewers.

Size: Length 6–22 mm.

Number of species: 50

Identification: Flattened, soft-bodied beetles with conspicuous, serrate^G antennae^G. These beetles are usually brown to orange in colour with black markings. Wing cases are parallel-sided or broadly expanded and leaf-like, with characteristic longitudinal ridges and a network of minor ridges.

Lycus constrictus

Lycus constrictus

Where found: On flowers and plants.

Habits: Active by day. They often congregate on flowers to feed and mate. They are probably distasteful to predators and are mimicked^G by various other insects.

Food: Adults feed on plant juices and small insects. Larvae feed on other insects.

Life history: Eggs are laid on the bark of dead trees. Larvae search for prey below bark and in rotten wood. They pupate^G below bark.

Ladybirds

Order Coleoptera (family: Coccinellidae)

Afrikaans name: Skilpadkewers.

Size: Length 0,5–10 mm.

Number of species: 245

Identification: Round beetles, usually red or orange with black markings; some are black marked with red or yellow.

Where found: On plants, especially those infested with aphids.

Habits: Ladybirds drop to the ground when disturbed and exude a poisonous, yellow fluid if handled. Their bright colours are a warning of their unpleasant taste. Many species gather in large numbers in rock crevices at the tops of hills, or sometimes in buildings, to pass the winter.

Food: Adults and larvae feed mostly on aphids; also scale insects, ants and thrips (not included in this guide). Species of the subfamily Epilachninae feed on foliage.

Life history: Yellow eggs are laid in batches on plants close to a food supply. The spiny, spindle-shaped larvae are black with bright markings. They pupate[G] on the plant where they feed.

Cheilomenes lunata

Toktokkies

Order Coleoptera (family: Tenebrionidae; Tentyriinae)

Tribe: Molurini (subtribes: Phanerotomina and Molurina).

Afrikaans name: Toktokkie.

Size: Length 10–65 mm.

Number of species: Several hundred.

Identification: Stout, globular beetles with long legs, some resembling ground beetles (Carabidae). Bodies are either smooth or heavily sculptured. Wing cases are fused together, so they cannot fly. They are mostly black or dark brown in colour.

Psammodes striatus

Where found: On the ground.

Habits: They are best known for their habit of tapping the ground with their abdomens, each species with its own rhythm. The taps serve as communication between the sexes.

Food: Dead plant and animal material.

Life history: Eggs are laid in the soil. Larvae look like mealworms, feeding underground on plant litter and roots. They pupate[G] in the soil.

Comments: Tenebrionidae (darkling beetles) is an enormous and very varied family (3 200 species occur in southern Africa!). It includes many fascinating desert-adapted species; others are pests that raid stored foods.

Blister Beetles/CMR Beetles

Order Coleoptera (family: Meloidae)

Afrikaans name: Blaartrekkewers, CMR-kewers.

Size: Length 5–40 mm.

Number of species: 346

Identification: Elongate, soft-bodied beetles, usually black with red or yellow bands. The head is relatively large and separated from the similar-sized pronotum[G] by a distinct neck. When folded, the wing cases are more-or-less parallel-sided.

Where found: On flowers and foliage.

Habits: Bright colours warn that these insects are distasteful and poisonous. A liquid, containing the poison cantharidin, is exuded if the beetles are handled. This can blister the skin and, if eaten, can even cause death. They are slow-flying, often congregating in numbers on flowers, where they feed and mate.

Food: Adults feed on flowers and foliage. Larvae feed on grass-hopper egg-pods or the juvenile stages of bees.

Life history: Eggs are laid in holes in the ground dug by the female. The first larval stage is active and searches for grasshopper eggs. Some bee-parasitizing ones wait on flowers to hitch a lift with bees and are carried back to the host's nest. If successful they turn into sluggish larva-like grubs which feed on the hosts. This is known as 'hypermetamorphosis'. Mature larvae eventually pupate[G] and emerge as adults during the rains.

Mylabris oculata

Longicorn Beetles

Order Coleoptera (family: Cerambycidae)

Afrikaans name: Boktorre.

Size: Length 3–100 mm.

Number of species: 650

Identification: Most species have elongate, cylindrical bodies with very long antennae^G, often much longer than the body. Antennae^G are swept back over the body when at rest. Mandibles are large and strong. Night-flying species are brownish, whereas those active by day often have bright, sometimes metallic, colours.

Where found: On flowers, foliage and the branches of trees (day-flying species), or under logs or bark (night-flying species).

Habits: Night-flying species are often attracted to light. They can produce sounds by rubbing the pronotum^G against the back.

Food: Adults feed on pollen or bark; larvae feed on wood.

Life history: Eggs are laid in cracks, or holes made by the female, in the stems or roots of woody plants. The long, cylindrical larvae bore into the host plant and may take several years to mature. They pupate^G in a chamber in the host plant.

Philomatium natalense

Tortoise Beetles

Order Coleoptera (family: Chrysomelidae; Cassidinae)

Afrikaans name: Klatergoud-kewers.

Size: Length 5–20 mm.

Number of species: 90

Identification: Flattened beetles with expanded wing cases, giving them the appearance of a tortoise. Some have a beautiful metallic gold lustre.

Where found: On foliage.

Habits: The larva accumulates the shrivelled skins from previous moults on its spiny, forked tail, which is held over its back.

Food: Leaves.

Life history: Eggs are laid singly on foliage and may be concealed with a cover of excreta. The mature larva attaches itself to a leaf where it pupates^G within the larval skin, emerging later as the adult beetle.

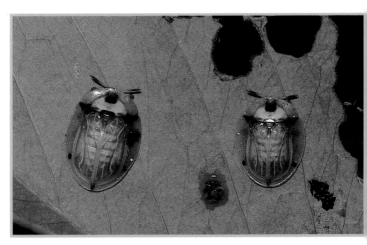

Aspidomorpha puncticosta

ily Weevils

Order Coleoptera (family: Curculionidae; Brachycerinae)

Afrikaans name: Leliesnuitkewers.

Size: Length 5–60 mm.

Number of species: Hundreds.

Identification: Robust, strongly sculptured, mostly brownish beetles, though some have coloured patterns. Like all weevils, the head is produced into a snout (rostrum) with the mouthparts at the end. The antennae^G are elbowed. They have fused wing cases and cannot fly.

Where found: Usually crawling on the ground or on lilies and aloes.

Brachycerus ornatus

Habits: Slow-moving beetles that feign death if touched or attacked. Some species are very long-lived, up to 30 years.

Food: Adults feed on the leaves of bulbs, aloes and related plants. Larvae feed on the bulbs and growing points of aloes.

Life history: Eggs are laid in the crowns of lilies and aloes. Larvae bore downwards during feeding, eventually destroying the host plant or demolishing the bulb. They pupate^G within the remains of the bulb or in the soil nearby.

Similar insects: Other weevils, which are very varied in size and habits and often with much longer snouts. Some species can fly. All eat plant material and are found mostly on plants. Some are pests, devouring stored grains.

Horse Flies

Order Diptera (family: Tabanidae)

Afrikaans name: Blindevlieë.

Size: Length 10–25 mm.

Number of species: 227

Identification: These are stout-bodied, fast-flying flies with large, flattened, semi-spherical heads and eyes. The latter are banded or spotted with iridescent colours. Wings may be patterned with dark markings. A few have very long prosoces[G].

Where found: Visiting flowers, flying around mammals and resting on tree trunks.

Habits: Females are well known for their silent attacks on humans and painful bites. They are most active on warm, sunny days.

Food: Adults feed on nectar and pollen; females also feed on mammalian blood. Larvae feed on insects and small invertebrates[G]; a few species feed on plant matter.

Life history: Eggs are laid on vegetation or stones in damp places near water. On hatching, the larvae burrow into the soil, where they hunt for prey. The fully grown larva pupates[G] in a cell just below the surface of the soil.

Haematopota sp.

Robber Flies

Order Diptera (family: Asilidae)

Afrikaans name: Roofvlieë.

Size: Length 3–40 mm.

Number of species: 500

Identification: Black or brownish flies, sometimes with pale markings. The head is hollowed out between well-separated, bulging eyes. The mouthparts form a prominent stiletto-like proboscis^G projecting forwards. There is a beard of bristles on the face. The body is either long and tapering or short and bee-like. Legs are strong and spiny for catching and holding insects. The wings are either clear, smoky or have dark patches.

Microstylum sp.

Where found: Resting on vegetation or on the ground.

Habits: They perch on prominent viewpoints and dart after insects flying past, returning to the perch to feed on the victim, which is stabbed and sucked dry through the strong proboscis^G.

Food: Other insects.

Life history: Eggs are laid in a wide variety of situations. Larvae live and pupate^G in the soil, in leaf litter or in rotting wood, scavenging or feeding on various stages of other insects.

Bee Flies

Order Diptera (family: Bombyliidae)

Afrikaans name: Byvlieë.

Size: Length 3–30 mm.

Number of species: 939

Identification: Hairy, stout-bodied flies that look like bees. They have a long, thin proboscis[G] which projects forwards, and slender, delicate legs. Wings may be clear or attractively marked.

Where found: Hovering over or resting on flowers or bare ground in bright sunshine.

Habits: They sound and look like bees when hovering. They are able to shoot eggs into the entrances of open burrows and the nests of solitary bees and wasps while hovering over them.

Food: Adults feed on pollen and nectar. Larvae feed on the eggs of grasshoppers, or larvae of solitary bees and wasps, beetles, moths and other flies.

Life history: Eggs are laid near the host or in the hosts' nests. Larvae are at first active and search for their host. They then moult into inactive maggots: another example of 'hypermetamorphosis' (see Blister Beetles). Mature maggots pupate[G] below the soil surface or within their hosts' nests.

Bombylius analis

Hover Flies

Order Diptera (family: Syrphidae)

Afrikaans name: Sweefvlieë.

Size: Length 3–18 mm.

Number of species: 226

Identification: Wasp- and bee-like flies, often brightly coloured with yellow bands or spots on a dark background. Large eyes cover most of head.

Where found: Hovering over flowers in bright sunshine or settling on damp soil.

Habits: These insects hover with ultra-precision, wings almost invisible, remaining motionless until darting to a new position.

Food: Nectar and pollen.

Life history: Eggs are laid according to the feeding habits of the larvae which eat insects, especially aphids, plant tissue, or dead animal or plant material; some scavenge in the nests of social bees, wasps and ants. Others are aquatic with long breathing tubes ('rat-tailed maggots').

Asarkina sp.

Blow Flies

Order Diptera (family: Calliphoridae)

Afrikaans name: Skaapbrommers.

Size: Length 6–15 mm.

Number of species: 145

Identification: Stout-bodied, commonly metallic blue or green flies.

Where found: Around carcasses, on excrement or indoors at windows. Also on flowers.

Habits: Adults are attracted in large numbers to carcasses, excrement, meat, fish and cooked cabbage. Some are parasites of livestock, laying eggs in open wounds. Putsi flies attack humans the larvae feeding under the skin. Others parasitise nests of solitary wasps or grasshopper egg pods. Some species are of forensic[G] value in estimating the time of death of carcasses and corpses.

Food: Fluids from carcasses, meat or excrement; also nectar.

Life history: Eggs hatch rapidly. Larvae eject saliva onto food, dissolving it and sucking up the resulting 'soup'. When mature many species pupate[G] in soil near larval habitat.

Chrysomya sp.

Similar insects: Flesh Flies (not included in this guide) (family Sarcophagidae) are grey and black, often chequered. They give birth to live young. Tachinid Flies (not included in this guide) (family Tachinidae) are very bristly. They parasitise other insects.

Butterflies and Moths

Order Lepidoptera

Afrikaans name: Skoenlappers, motte.

Size: Wingspan 3–190 mm.

Number of species: About 10 000.

Identification: Adults have four membranous wings covered with tiny scales, either brightly coloured (most butterflies and day-flying moths) or drab (many moths). Mouthparts form a long tube for sucking up liquids, coiled up when not in use. At rest wings are usually held vertically in butterflies. Moths hold them roof-wise over the body, hugging the body or held out sideways, against the substrate. Larvae, or caterpillars (see p. 7), have distinct heads and chewing mouthparts; three pairs of jointed true legs on the thorax and up to five pairs of fleshy false legs on the abdomen. Their soft bodies may be covered with spines or dense hairs.

Where found: Various habitats.

Habits: Butterflies are day-flying,

Imbrasia belina

visiting flowers for nectar. Most moths are night-flying resting on vegetation during the day, often relying on camouflage to hide.

Food: Larvae eat foliage or other parts of plants. Some species eat human foods, wool, horn and even wax in bee-hives. Adults drink nectar, plant sap or fluids arising from excrement or over-ripe fruit; some species do not feed at all.

Life history: Females lay eggs on plants or food sources specific to their species. Mature moth larvae pupate[G] in a silken cocoon attached to the foodplant or other support, in an earthen cell or in a cavity within a plant stem. The butterfly pupa[G], or chrysalis, has no cocoon and is attached posteriorly to the food-plant or a support, hanging down-wards or held up by a silken girdle.

Spider-Hunting Wasps

Order Hymenoptera (family: Pompilidae)

Afrikaans name:
Spinnekopjagters.

Size: Length 4–55 mm.

Number of species: At least 200.

Identification: Active, long-legged wasps with glossy blue or black bodies, sometimes with yellow or orange markings. Wings are black with a blue sheen, orange to red, or transparent.

Where found: Visiting flowers or on the ground.

Habits: Females run about on the ground, flicking and jerking their wings. Some large species make a loud clicking noise when flying.

Food: Nectar (adults); captured spiders (larva).

Life history: Females hunt and paralyse spiders, which they use to feed their young. One spider is placed in each nest, which may be a mud nest built in a cavity, a burrow dug in the ground or the spider's own burrow. After laying one egg on the spider the nest is sealed and abandoned. The larva feeds on this provision and then pupates[G] within the cell. The emerging adult chews its way out.

Comments: Females deliver a very painful sting.

Tachypompilus ignitus

Paper Wasps

Order Hymenoptera (family: Vespidae)

Afrikaans name: Perdebye.

Size: Length 7–35 mm.

Number of species: 35

Identification: The fore-wings of paper wasps fold longitudinally when at rest. Most species are slender wasps, with short or long waists. Usually brown, sometimes with yellow markings or bands.

Where found: On foliage, flowers, and on paper nests attached to plants or buildings.

Habits: These are social wasps, raising their young in many-celled nests made from wood-pulp and saliva. The nests are aggressively defended against intruders.

Food: Nectar and juices from over-ripe fruit.

Life history: Eggs are laid singly in cells. Larvae are fed directly with chewed-up caterpillars, by the adults. When mature, they pupate[G]

Belonogaster dubia

in their cells. Emerging females remain on the nest, helping with day-to-day activities. Colonies break up in autumn. Mated females pass the winter in sheltered places and found new colonies in spring.

Similar insects: Potter and mason wasps (family Eumenidae), which are solitary, and build their nests with mud.

Comments: Some species are often called hornets.

Mason and Potter Wasps

Order Hymenoptera (family: Eumenidae)

Afrikaans name: Pleisterperdebye, pottebakkerwespe.

Size: Length 4–35 mm.

Number of species: A few hundred.

Delta lepeleterii

Identification: The fore-wings fold longitudinally when at rest. Most species are slender, with short or long waists, some brownish, others black and yellow or black with red or white tips to the abdomens.

Where found: Visiting flowers, attending mud nests or burrowing in the ground, or found at water.

Habits: These wasps build mud nests of one or more cells on boulders, tree trunks, leaves and buildings, or make cells in burrows dug in the ground or in pre-existing cavities in branches, twigs or timber structures. The entrances of some nests have funnelled rims for guiding the caterpillar food into the cell. Some burrow nesters and cavity nesters have mud turrets attached to the nest entrance.

Food: Nectar.

Life history: Each egg is suspended from the roof of its cell by a thread. The cell is then provisioned with several caterpillars before being sealed. Others – *Synagris*, for example – feed each larva until it is fully grown before starting the next cell. The larva pupates[G] within its cell; emerging adults chew their way out.

Similar insects: Mud daubers (family Sphecidae) eg. *Sceliphron spirifex*, which provision nests with spiders. The egg is attached to the prey. There is no funnelled entrance to the nest.

Mud Daubers/Digger Wasps

Order Hymenoptera (family: Sphecidae)

Afrikaans name: Graafwespe, kleiwespe.

Size: Length 1–45 mm.

Number of species: 740

Identification: Variable in appearance; some species are short-waisted, and others are long-waisted. Black, black-and-yellow, brown, metallic blue and green are the most common colours. Wings are often clear, with no longitudinal fold. Females may have a comb-like structure on each fore-leg for digging and raking sand.

Where found: Visiting flowers or on the ground in open, sandy locations; mud daubers are found in buildings, or collecting mud.

Habits: Most dig burrows in the ground or nest in pre-existing cavities or hollow stems. Some build mud nests. Each nest may have one or more cells, each of which is provisioned with one or several paralysed insects or

Bembix sp.

spiders. Each species has its own kind of prey.

Food: Nectar.

Life history: One egg is attached to one of the prey in each cell. After eating all the food supply, the larva pupates^G within the nest. Emerging adults chew their way out.

Similar insects: Potter and mason wasps, and paper wasps, which have a longitudinal fold in each fore-wing.

Carpenter Bees

Order Hymenoptera (family: Anthophoridae; Xylocopinae)

Afrikaans name: Houtkapperbye.

Size: Length 10–35 mm.

Number of species: 126

Identification: Rotund bees, usually black and often with bands of conspicuous yellow or white hairs, or with red hairs on the thorax. Males of some species are uniformly covered with yellow or rufous hairs.

Where found: Visiting flowers, flying around bushes, trees, dead branches and timber structures.

Habits: Females bore wide tunnels in dry, rotten wood, or in thick plant stems, in which they place cells end-to-end. Each cell is provisioned with a pollen and nectar mixture. Females guard their burrows, flying aggressively round an intruder.

Food: Nectar.

Life history: One egg is placed on top of the food mass in each cell. Mature larvae pupate[G] in their cells. On emerging, bees remain in the nest apart from occasional forays for food. Males are driven out in spring. Due to hostility, all but one of the females leave to start new burrows.

Xylocopa nigrita

Ants

Order Hymenoptera (family: Formicidae)

Afrikaans name: Miere.

Size: Length 1–20 mm.

Number of species: 593

Identification: Ants have a one- or two-segmented waist (petiole) between the thorax and abdomen. The head is modified according to caste[G]; soldier ants tend to have very large heads. The antennae[G] are characteristically elbowed. Workers and soldiers are wingless, sterile females. Males and reproductive females are more-or-less similar, but have wings. The colour ranges from black through brown to yellowish.

Where found: Everywhere, especially on the ground.

Habits: Ants are colonial insects, foraging in parties. They often tend honeydew-producing insects. Nests are underground, in rotten wood or in vegetation.

Food: Animal and plant material, living and dead.

Camponotus importunus

Life history: The winged males and females (alates) periodically leave the nests in mating flights. After mating, males die and females look for nesting sites. They then discard their wings and start new colonies. The eggs, larvae and pupae[G] are cared for by workers.

Similar insects: Termites, which are pale coloured, have no waist and have bead-like antennae[G]. Velvet ants (not included in this guide) are wingless female wasps, conspicuously coloured and solitary.

Comments: Ants are the most successful of social insects, with a wide range of nest structures, and a varied social life. They use many methods to obtain and store food.

Glossary

Antennae: Sensory, jointed structures on head.

Castes: Different types of individuals within the same species of social insect that are specialised for different tasks, such as workers, soldiers, kings and queens.

Cerci: Paired structures at the end of the abdomen, usually filamentous and segmented.

Compound eyes: Large lateral eyes, made up of many separate visual elements.

Cryptic: Of a concealing or camouflaging nature.

Dicotyledon: A plant whose embryo has two cotyledons (food storage organs); includes all woody plants that produce flowers.

Femur: Third section of insect leg.

Forensic: Having application in criminal investigations.

Invertebrates: Animals without backbones e.g. earthworms, snails, centipedes, millipedes, spiders, mites, scorpions, woodlice.

Mimicry: Close resemblance of one species of organism to another

Ovipositor: Organ used for laying eggs.

Proboscis: Extended, elongate mouth structure.

Pronotum: Upper surface of the prothorax.

Prothorax: Front section of the thorax.

Pupa: Inactive, non-feeding stage between larva and adult in holometabolous insects.

Pupate: Process of changing into a pupa.

Raptorial: Adapted for seizing prey.

Serrate: Saw-like.

Stridulate: To produce sound by rubbing one part of the body against another.

Tibia: Fourth section of insect leg.